I'M SORRY!

Copyright © 2010 by Hans Wilhelm, Inc.

All rights reserved. Published by Scholastic Inc.
SCHOLASTIC, CARTWHEEL BOOKS, NOODLES, and associated logos
are trademarks and/or registered trademarks of Scholastic Inc.
Lexile is a registered trademark of MetaMetrics, Inc.

Library of Congress Cataloging-in-Publication Data is available.

ISBN 978-0-545-24504-3

12 11 10 9 8 7 6 5 4 3 2 1   10 11 12 13 14 15/0

Printed in the U.S.A. 40 • First printing, October 2010

noodles®

SCHOLASTIC READER
LEVEL 1
50-250 WORDS

I'M SORRY!

by Hans Wilhelm

Cartwheel
·B·O·O·K·S·®

SCHOLASTIC INC.

New York   Toronto   London   Auckland
Sydney   Mexico City   New Delhi   Hong Kong

Let's play tag!

I'm going to catch you!

Oops!

Get out of my way!

Oops!

Now I'll get you!

Come down.
I want to play!

What shall I do now?

I know.
I'll play with my friends.

Does anyone want to play catch?

What's wrong?
What did I do?

They are angry with me.
I should say sorry.

"I'm sorry."

They are still angry with me.
I have to try again.

"I'M REALLY SORRY!"

Are we friends again?

Yes, we are!